This book is not like other ~~books~~ you have
read. YOU will decide if you live or die
by making choices that affect how the
adventure unfolds.

Each section of this book is numbered.
At the end of most sections, you will have
to make a choice. The choice you make will
take you to a different section of the book.

Some of your choices will help you
to survive the adventure. But choose
carefully! The wrong decisions could cost
you your life...

If you die, then go back to the chapter
number you are given and learn from your
mistake.

If you choose correctly, you will survive.

CHAPTER ONE

When the driver of the car you are travelling in sees a line of demonstrators blocking the street ahead, he slams on the brakes. He puts his car into reverse — just in time. Petrol bombs arc over the crumbling police line. They burst into flames as the fuel-filled bottles smash on the road among the helmeted officers. You see a police man's flak jacket set on fire and watch as two of his fellow officers break from their shield wall. They roll him over and over to smother the flames.

The crowd sees its chance, and in seconds it sweeps through the gap in the police line and into the street beyond.

The car is still reversing. You see fear on the driver's face as he cranes his neck back and swings the car around, tyres screeching. For a second he fumbles with the gears. Now your window is facing the mass of angry people and you can read the placards. "Give us the Serum" one says. Another reads "Cure us now". Finally, when it seems that the car will never move, the driver crunches the gearstick into place and you speed away.

In the back, the driver's sick wife and child stare ahead blankly. The woman's head snaps back as the car accelerates. A line of vomit trails out of her half-open mouth as her head lolls back. In the firelight the vomit looks like blood, but that thought has little time to register when you see what's ahead.

There's a dark blue police riot control

vehicle (RCV). Its turret is turning to face the rioters — and the car you are in. The noise of sirens and volume-distorted instructions through loudspeakers fills the air. You're heading towards the RCV. You glance round at the driver next to you, and remember how — just minutes earlier — your dad stopped him in the street, pulled open the door of the car, and pushed you inside with a handful of cash. You notice now that the driver is wide-eyed and unfocused. Has the fever struck him too?

You grab the steering wheel and yank it hard right, just in time. The nearside wing of the car clips the RCV's front wheel. Then the RCV fires its water cannon, the full force blasting your car half off its wheels, then slamming it down with a shove that scoots the car clean away.

The driver has the wheel again. He has

control for now as you power down an empty street, but you can see that the sweat streaming down his face is not just from his terror; the virus has taken hold and he won't last long now.

You talk to him. Keep him awake. Do anything necessary to keep him driving.

"What's your name?" you ask.

"Peter."

"Turn left here. Now right. Get onto the through route — out of town."

He follows your instructions without question — you don't let him look back.

"This way now. You're doing fine."

The last thing Dad said when he pushed

you into the car was to make for your aunt Alex's farmhouse outside the city. The man — Peter — had said it was on his way when Dad had given him the money, but since then things had gone mad. Everyone had known the mutated flu virus was coming — the one without a cure. Since the first cases ripped their way through the south coast seaports just two weeks ago, no-one talked of anything else. All work in the country had stopped. School stopped. People stocked up with food from the supermarkets and went back to their families to hide.

But then nothing happened. Cases of the sickness went down. Against all the predictions, very few people had actually died. Gradually, everyone left their seclusion and went back to their lives — which, as it turned out, was exactly the wrong thing to do. During those two quiet weeks the virus had been multiplying inside its hosts. All it needed was contact with more people to spread the contagion — and so the number of cases exploded.

The government could do very little except broadcast "Go to your homes, take aspirin and drink lots of water" and "Listen out for more news bulletins". That's when anarchy set in. When people decide they are going to die, they have nothing to lose. Some demonstrated in the streets for a cure. Some looked to religion. Others smashed up the cities, looting the shops for anything they could take on the grounds that even with the worst epidemic, there are always some people that survive. And in that madness, you were sent away. Dad said that as you weren't ill, you had to get somewhere safe before the virus took hold of you.

Survival Challenge: Taking Control

But now Peter is losing control again. You're on the main road, heading out of town and it's getting dark. Peter's driving fast — too fast — and if you don't slow down quickly, you'll hit the van in front of you.

Suddenly Peter's head slumps forward onto the steering wheel. You have to act now!

The decisions you make now will decide whether you live or die.

   To shake him to wake him up, go to 22.
   To try to remove the car key, go to 38.
   To grab the wheel, go to 61.

1.

You shout out, "Hello!" The women carry on running and reach the farmhouse. You can see them, and others, looking at you from behind the windows. At the door there is a man with a scarf over his mouth. He is holding a handgun.

To approach with caution, go to 50.

To run towards the house, go to 34.

To stop where you are, go to 8.

2.

The intense cold clouds your mind. You feel warm. You need to sleep. Hypothermia has got you. You drift off and never wake up.

You haven't survived! Get back to Chapter 5 to try the challenge again.

3.

You're still gaining on the van in front of you. Time is running out!

To shout at Peter, go to 26.

To punch Peter, and then grab the steering wheel, go to 31.

To try pulling the handbrake, go to 40.

4.

Continuing forward into the shop, you find

packets of cornflakes and a turned-off refrigerator cabinet full of packs of meat, cheese and cartons of milk. It really stinks now. You think you hear a slight scrape or shuffling sound in the dark ahead.

➜ If you want to go back to investigate the counter and aisle, go to 48.

➜ If you want to push ahead, go to 58.

5.

The ice cracks under the deer and it plunges into the water.

➜ To call Wolf back, go to 69.

➜ To let him follow the deer, go to 18.

➜ To go after the deer yourself, go to 86.

6.

You run back the way you came, but now the dogs have something to chase, and they're after you! More dogs appear from an alleyway to your right, growling and snarling. There must be at least six, plus the three behind you.

➡ To stand and fight the dogs, go to 52.

➡ To dart left in to the electrical shop window with the van smashed half through it, go to 45.

7.

Whiley steps forward onto the doormat to get a better angle. He fires off a burst from his automatic rifle into the side of the barn behind you.

➡ To move further behind the fuel drums, go to 49.

➡ If you want to shout to Wolf, "Come here boy!", go to 37.

➡ To set fire to the fuel — and if you are feeling lucky — go to either 15 or 60.

8.

You come to an abrupt halt. A second man — tall, long-haired with a leather coat, and armed with a military-type automatic rifle — comes to the door. "We don't want you here," he shouts, levelling the gun at you.

➡ If you want to talk to him to persuade him to let you in, go to 54.

➡ If you'd rather run away, go to 76.

9.

You chase along the riverbank past a partly fallen tree and towards a large oak with low branches that stick far over the river. The panicked deer is being swept right towards you.

➡ To grip onto the branches and try to stab the deer with your knife as it comes past, go to 51.

➡ To lasso its antlers with your rope is going to require some luck, go to either 35 or 46.

➡ To just watch as the river sweeps it past you, go to 67.

10.

Only luck will decide whether you or the pack get to the door first. Choose either 24 or 47.

11.

In amongst the scattered boxes you find a torch set and batteries. You soon have the

9

10

11

torch out and working.

➜   If you want to use it to look around at the tins on the shelves in the aisle, go to 82.

➜   If you'd prefer to move further into the shop, go to 58.

12.
You run out onto the ice and it gives way under your feet. You, Wolf and the deer are swept into the river. Go to 65.

13.
The car begins to spin across the road — just as a fuel tanker appears around the corner. There is a crunch of metal as you crash together. Glass smashes around you, before the road is engulfed in a fireball.

➜   You have failed to survive. If you're up for the challenge, get back to Chapter 1.

14.
You run forwards, but the dogs are catching up. Behind you, Wolf is snapping at the

lead dogs, but it's clear that while he can probably look after himself, you are not going to be able to outrun the pack.

➡ To stand and fight the pack, go to 52.

➡ To hide in a car, go to 84.

➡ To run back to the electrical shop with the van sticking through the window you'll have to take a chance. Choose either 24 or 45.

15.

Whoompf! the fuel ignites, and a ball of flame shoots upwards. Whiley turns away as he shields himself from the heat.

➡ To hide further behind the drums, go to 49.

➡ To call for Wolf to "Come, boy!" go to 55.

16.

Sharp dog jaws bite at your neck and shoulder and claws rake across your chest. The massive dog leaps forward again,

15

16

but is pulled to an abrupt stop by a chain attached to its collar. Unfortunately, now it has you cornered against a shelf stacked with cans.

➜ To go forward into the darkness to try to get past the dog, go to 64.

➜ To try hitting the dog with your hammer, go to 79.

➜ To open one of the cans and feed the contents to the dog, go to 21.

17.

You push down the clutch, while controlling the car with the steering wheel. The car slowly rolls to a stop with its engine still revving noisily. You keep one foot on the clutch and grab Peter's leg to move his foot off the accelerator. You push his lifeless body out of the way and pull the key from the ignition. The engine falls silent. You made it!

You get out of the car and lean on the

bodywork, shaking while the shock kicks in. Peter is unconscious. His wife and kid look unconscious; they might be dead. If they aren't now, then they will be soon. That's one thing you know for certain. If the virus infects someone, then it's a death sentence. Are you infected? You're feeling a bit warm, but that might just be the panic. You begin to walk along the road. It's getting dark when you start to feel dizzy...

CHAPTER TWO

Everything is blurred and upside down. There's a cold breeze against your cheek, and you can hear curtains swishing.

You're awake, so you must be alive. You

lift your head, which was lolling over the edge of the bed, and the world turns the right way up. You're in a bedroom, but not a bedroom that you know. There are dead flowers in a vase and porcelain ornaments on a dresser. There's no sound — no radio playing downstairs, no noise of cars going past, just the rustle of leaves in the wind through an open window, nothing more.

Snippets of memory slowly drift back; you remember walking by the road with dazzling headlights speeding past. You had a headache so bad it felt like someone was drilling into your skull. Then a door was opening and an old lady said you were burning up; she put wet flannels on your forehead that made you go suddenly cold and slimy with sweat. You can't remember seeing her after that. The chills made your teeth chatter. You wrapped yourself in a duvet and you're embarrassed to recall you cried out. But no one answered.

You shuffle out and find the bathroom. When you try the taps, water only comes from the hot tap, and it's cold.

"Hello!" you say loudly.

"HELLO! Anyone there?" you shout.

You drift into another bedroom. Wardrobe doors have been left open, a drawer has been pulled out of a cabinet, and there are discarded clothes scattered on the bed. On the wall you notice two unfaded squares on the wallpaper where pictures have been removed.

"HELLO!" you shout again, but it doesn't surprise you when no-one answers.

Hungry.

You head downstairs to find the kitchen. A reek of rotten food hits you when you open the fridge and the light does not come on. You find some bread. It's fuzzy with green mould. How long have you been asleep?

Your thoughts turn to contacting your family. Ring Dad — he'll be worried! Ring Alex. You fumble around in your pockets for your mobile. The battery is dead. Typical! You try the old lady's landline. There is no dialling tone. Nothing. Not even hissing.

A wave of sadness hits you. Your parents are probably worrying about you, and you can't make contact. You know that it's irrational to let your emotions screw you up. You must think clearly and decide what to do next. You need food. You're going to have to go out and find a shop. You scout around for anything useful and find a hammer in a cupboard under the stairs. You have a feeling it might come in handy.

Outside in the sunshine there is no traffic on the road. There are cars parked at some of the houses nearby. None of them are just abandoned with doors open, or dead bodies hanging out like in the movies. So, you think, the people must be all right, mustn't they?

You shout really loud to get some attention. No one comes out, so you go up to the nearest house and look through the front window. There is a woman lying down in her living room. She doesn't react when you tap on the glass. She just carries on staring with open eyes that don't blink.

You run when you realise she's dead.

Not far down the road you come to a small shop. It's closed, with its security shutter pulled down across the windows and door. On closer inspection the shutter is secured at the bottom with a strong-looking padlock. You know there's food in there, and you throw some stones at the upstairs windows to get the owner's attention. No one comes. You know that nobody will stop you if you smash the padlock and go in, but you still wait. What you are doing is wrong, but you are hungry.

You argue with yourself — forcing your way into a shop with nobody in it has got to be better than breaking into one of the houses. Plus you'd be more likely to find a sick person in a house, or even worse — dead bodies. You decide to get the job done as quickly as possible.

Survival Challenge: Robbing the Shop

You use the hammer to lever up the bottom of the security shutters. Then you smash through the glass door until you've made a hole big enough to get through safely. It's dark inside. You can just see a counter on your left. Ahead is an aisle with magazines, newspapers and some tins on shelves. The shop stinks of meat that's gone off.

The decisions you make now will decide whether you live or die.

➜   If you want to investigate the counter and aisle on the left, go to 48.
➜   If you want to go forward down the aisle, go to 4.

18.
Wolf and the deer are both in the water, struggling to keep their heads above the surface as they are washed downstream. Go to 9.

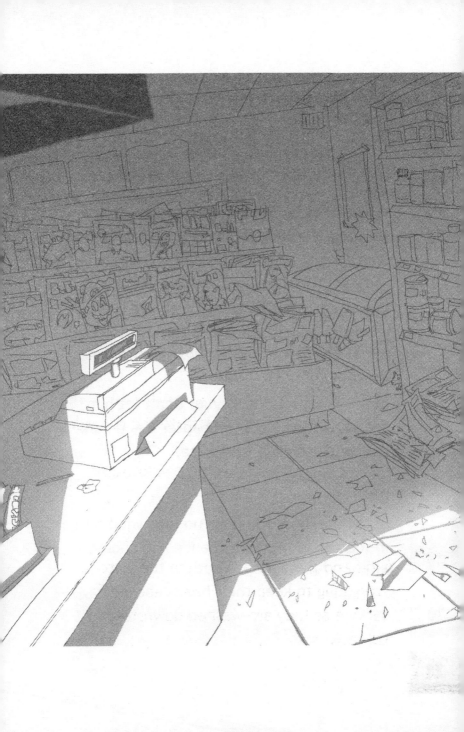

19.

A gunshot rings out, kicking up a spurt of dust by your feet. Go to 80.

20.

Wolf rushes at Whiley, pulling away the gatepost blocking the wheel, and the lorry starts to roll. The trap has been sprung too early! The lasso pulls away uselessly in front of Whiley's feet. He smirks as he levels his gun at you and fires an automatic burst. The last thing you hear is Laura screaming.

➜   Whiley has killed you! Don't let him get away — go back to Chapter 6 and make a different choice next time.

21.

In the darkness you have no idea what is in the can. So, take a chance and choose either 27 or 53.

22.

You grab Peter's shoulder and shake him. It seems to work. He lifts his head up and notices just in time that he is about to crash into the van. He swerves over onto the other side of the road. Go to 56.

23.

The deer makes to jump but the pressure on the ice is too much. It breaks off, pitching the deer into the freezing water. Go to 69.

24.

You run for it and Wolf leaps out into the pack. You swing your axe, knocking two dogs aside, but then one locks onto your arm and you drop your weapon. You kick out, but dogs are ripping your clothes and tearing at your skin. You hear Wolf yelp with pain as you fall into the pack.

➜ You made a bad choice and have paid with your life. Are you still hungry for the challenge? Of course you are — get back to Chapter 3.

25.

The dog bolts past you, and out of the shop through the gap in the shutter. It looks like it was just scared. Go to 33.

26.

You try shouting at Peter, but the virus has taken hold. The car smashes into the back of the van in front. The tyres screech. The car you are in slows down! Go to 13.

27.

Quickly, you pull the tab on a can and throw the contents at the dog. It feeds greedily on the tinned meat, giving you the chance to grab some supplies, including bottled water, cola, chocolate bars, packet rice and some dried fruit. Suddenly there is a loud crash as the dog slips from the chain and bounds out under the shop shutter. Go to 33.

28.

You pull the wheel, and the car kicks up stones as it heads off the road. But you're still going too fast! The car skids down into a ditch with a sickening crunch.

➡ You die slowly in a pool of stinking

water. Go back to Chapter 1 to begin the challenge again.

29.
The deer is close to death. It floats limp in the current and you manage to edge it into the shallows. Success! The meat from this deer will feed you all for at least a week. Go to 78.

30.
You leap out from behind the fuel drums and Whiley shoots at you, but his gun jams. Go to 90.

31.
You punch Peter and he releases the steering wheel. You grab it and guide the car past the van. Go to 81.

32.
The engine over-revs as it disconnects from the drive, but you're still driving towards

the lorry at over 60 kph. The car smashes into it and you are killed instantly.

➜ You failed the challenge. Go back to Chapter 1, and start again.

33.

Soon you are sitting on a wall outside, stuffing yourself with chocolate and drinking cans of unchilled cola. You have filled two plastic bags with enough food to last about three days. You flick through a newspaper. Many of the stories are about the virus, complaining about the government reaction. Somewhere else it says that the virus might be the work of terrorists. But what interests you most is an article by a doctor that says some people survive even the worst epidemics. They have a natural immunity, a million-to-one gene that means they can't get ill. Are you that "lucky" person? Your thoughts turn to what has happened to the rest of your family...

CHAPTER THREE

You've made a decision about what to do.
The only way to stop thinking about what
has happened to Mum, Dad and your sister,
Laura, is to go home and find out. You think
the journey will take about two or three
days, if you can find a bicycle. You'll need
something other than plastic bags to carry
your supplies in, too. And how will you get
these things? Burglary, of course!

Getting into the first house is easy
enough. You just hammer in the glass of
the front door, and crawl through, but once
inside the smell hits you, and you throw
up chocolate and cola all over the carpet.
You rush outside and gulp down lungfuls of
sweet fresh air.

Dead bodies stink. It's a smell you know from when you and Dad once found a sheep carcass in a field; a gone-off meaty stench that made you wrinkle your nose and turn away in disgust. Human bodies smell of pork: rancid, rotten, putrid, maggot-ridden dead pig. Gases build up in the corpses so they bloat up and bulge. When the skin ruptures, the stench is vile and in the enclosed spaces of rooms that have been shut up for days, that stink is super-concentrated.

Before you try the next house, you wrap your hoodie around your nose and mouth. Inside you find more packets of food, a long knife and an axe. Searching in cupboards upstairs, you pick up a rucksack and a sleeping bag. The smell is worse up here and you soon find out why. A whole family — mother, father and three small children — are wrapped in a grisly

death embrace on the parents' double bed.
The children just look as if they are asleep.
You find yourself thinking of Mum, Dad
and Laura and quickly turn and race down
the stairs with your stuff. You come to a
sudden stop.

The guard dog from the shop is back. It's standing inside the front door; it obviously heard you stomping down the stairs. You reach for your knife, but the dog shies away. If it wasn't half-starved it would be a fine animal — at least part Alsatian — a dog that could really look after itself. You decide to open a can of meat and toss the contents through the smashed door, out into the street. The dog bounds after it. You slip out of the house, but when you turn round, the dog is padding along behind you dragging its chain. You seem to have earned a loyal friend.

The next day the dog brings you a lamb he has killed, so you give him a name, "Wolf". The dog's the only company you've got, and soon you are talking to Wolf. You remove the chain from his neck and continue to feed him. It's not long before he never leaves your side.

A week passes, and despite finding a bicycle you still haven't reached your town. It's tougher going than you thought it would be, but at least you can follow the road signs. At night you sleep in empty cars because you can't bear to go into houses when it's dark. You've seen too many corpes already.

Then one day you start to recognise your surroundings — you're nearly home. You are following the school bus route when the bicycle gets a puncture. You leave it in the middle of the road and decide to walk the quick way through the town centre.

It's not long before you realise you've made a big mistake.

Survival Challenge: Escaping the Pack

The streets are empty, but as you reach the shopping centre it is clear there has been trouble here. Cars have been used as barricades across the street; some vehicles are burnt out. To your right a van has smashed through the window of an electrical shop.

Then you notice Wolf's ears prick up. He is tense and you notice him sniff the air. Before you can react, three dogs appear from behind one of the cars further down the street. You slowly slide your hand-axe out of your belt.

The decisions you make now will decide whether you live or die.

➜   If you want to turn and run back the way you have come, go to 6.

➜   If you want to make a dash for the shop window where the van has smashed through it, go to 45.

➜   If you want to get into the abandoned car right in front of you, go to 84.

➜   If you'd prefer to carry on moving down the street, go to 57.

34.

The man in the doorway shoots at you. Are you feeling lucky? Go to either 43 or 87.

35.

Your rope catches for an instant on one of the deer's antlers, but your shoes slip on the frosty ground and the sudden jolt pulls you into the water. Go to 65.

36.

You and Wolf sprint through the shop towards the fire exit. Dogs are barking as they rush after you through the broken window, closing in fast. You and Wolf have nearly made it to the door. You're level with the fire extinguisher now.

➜ If you want to throw the extinguisher at a dog, go to 74.

➜ If you want to set the extinguisher off, go to 62.

➜ If you'd rather keep running straight for the door, go to 10.

37.

Wolf runs towards you, bullets peppering the ground as you duck for cover. For a second, Wolf's lead pulls tight, then he pulls the gatepost free and the lorry begins to roll. Everything seems to happen in slow motion; the lorry rolls forward and the rope trailing from it starts to pull. You mustn't let Whiley realise what's about to

happen. You have to distract him.

→ To set light to the fuel, go to 63.

→ To make yourself a target, go to 70.

38.
You reach for the car key, but Peter is in the way. He is awake enough, and shoves you back into your seat. Go to 3.

39.
You push the clutch pedal down. The car doesn't really slow down, and it is still out of control. Go to 28.

40.
With the handbrake on the car spins, slowing you down. But you are out of control and the car clips the kerb. The car flips over. The final impact smashes the life out of your body.

→ You have died in a massive car crash. Start your challenge again at Chapter 1.

38

39

40

41.

You wait until later before making your move. The barking, growling and clawing at the car door has stopped and many of the dogs have retreated to the shade. Several dogs are under cars nearby, and there must be some underneath the car you are hiding in. The pack leader — a badly scarred Doberman — is asleep on the car bonnet. You click open the door and run. It takes a few seconds for the pack to react.

➜   If you want to fight off the pack with your axe and knife, go to 52.

➜   If you want to run for it, go to 24.

➜   If you want to run to the electrical shop with the van smashed through the window, go to 45.

42.

One of the deer's legs catches you in the chest, knocking the air from your lungs. You sink under the water. You try to pull yourself up to the surface but you are too cold — too weak. You breathe only water — and you drown.

➜   You have failed! Go back to Chapter 5 to try the Deer Hunt Challenge again.

43.

The bullet whizzes just over your head.

➜   If you want to carry on towards the farm house, go to 87.

➜   To stop and put your hands up, go to 8.

➜   If you want to run for it, go to 76.

44.

You pull the steering wheel and manage to get the car back on the road. Go to 81.

45.

You reach the window and pull yourself through between the jagged glass and the side of the van. You and Wolf scramble over some smashed-up shelving and into the shop. There's a counter with a cash register, and past that there's a

43

44

45

door marked "Fire Exit" with a CO_2 fire extinguisher hung up next to it. Wolf defends you, biting at dogs as they stick their heads into the shop. His fur is bloodied and you know he can't hold out much longer.

➡ To hide behind the counter with the cash register, go to 68.

➡ To stand and fight the dogs off, go to 52.

➡ To run for the door at the back of the shop, go to 36.

46.

With amazing strength or luck you manage to hold the deer against the water current. Soon its thrashing movements get weaker. A bedraggled Wolf appears. Go to 29.

47.

Luckily the door is not locked. You kick off a small mongrel that has attached its jaws to your leg and, with Wolf following, you push through into a dim space with a staircase leading upwards. As you pull the door shut behind you, you can hear growling and barking, and the scratching of dogs' claws on the wood. You sprint up the stairs and, after Wolf has bounded through, slam shut the door at the top.

CHAPTER FOUR

You find yourself in a corridor with closed doors on both sides. These open into storerooms containing office supplies and cans of cleaning fluid labelled "flammable". Another room is a staff kitchen with a few empty milk cartons, but nothing edible. In a cupboard you find a lighter.

At the rear of the building there's a fire

exit and another flight of stairs going up. You push the fire escape release bar and crack it open a fraction, revealing metal steps leading down to a delivery area. From there to the street, you would have to go through a side alley past the dogs out front.

You click the door shut and climb up the stairs; they lead to a flat roof that stretches the whole length of the row of shops. There is no way down from here. The only escape route seems to be through the fire exit, but if you're going to make it to the street alive, you will need some sort of diversion. This requires human ingenuity. You may not be fierce or have sharp teeth but, unlike a dog, you can throw things — and you have fire!

A plan quickly comes together in your head. Five minutes later, you are on the roof overlooking the street out front, armed with a pile of cardboard boxes and four milk cartons of cleaning fluid; ready to go.

First you set light to the boxes and toss them down into the street. You've soaked them with fluid so that they stay alight as they fall. The dogs avoid these easily but that's no problem, the boxes are just your fire starters. It's the bottles of cleaning fluid that really get things going. Just as the boxes are hitting the ground, you throw the "fire bombs". The cartons hit the ground and explode open, their contents instantly catching alight. Three dogs are swept up in a pool of fire and more are spattered nearby. The dogs are sent into a wild panic as they try to bite out the flames on their backs. But you have no time to stand and watch.

You speed through the fire exit, down the steps and out into the delivery area, followed closely by Wolf. This is clear, but you can see three dogs in the alley through to the street at the front. You don't have any fire bombs left! Wolf leaps in front of you, barking wildly, the fur on his back raised in anger. You run forward towards the dogs, shouting loudly and waving your axe. The noise is enough to make the dogs have second thoughts, and they turn tail and run. You run out into the street, only stopping when you've made four blocks' distance and are approaching the neighbourhood where you live.

Home. Breaking into your own house is a little more disturbing than those other houses. Inside it looks just the same as ever, but there's no one home.

What did you expect? The whole world

dies and your happy family is there waiting for you?

Your bedroom is still littered with stuff. Laura's bedroom too. It looks so pointless now, with all that's happened; a games console won't keep you alive. Quickly you find yourself following your new routine: raid the kitchen cupboards for cans and packets of food, drain out the water system for drinkable water. It's only when you brush against a photo of your family that any emotion kicks in.

That clean, well-groomed child in the picture is you. Was you. Even if you were to wash away the ingrained grime, your gaze would still be hard now, your smile never again so carefree. Mum, Dad and Laura are gone from here, and you have to leave too. There is nothing here for you now.

As you head for the garage to fetch your

BMX, you notice Wolf nosing at a lime green square of paper under the mirror in the hall. It's a Post-it note. Laura was always sticking them around the house. You snatch up the paper and immediately recognise your sister's tiny handwriting.

(Just in case you ever come home)
Alex rang and said you never got to her. Mum's been crying a lot, saying she should never have sent you away, and Dad keeps quiet and comforts her, but I know he's upset too. Alex said you were independently spirited, and she knows you'll get to Holme Park Farm somehow. She's driving down to collect me this afternoon. Mum and Dad say it's best that I go. Things really are going crazy around here.
I miss you.   *Laura*

You can't hold the tears in any longer, and you begin to cry as you head to the garage. You must get to Holme Park Farm.

Survival Challenge: Holme Park Farm

The cycle journey to Alex's takes days. It's mostly uphill and slow going, but you finally arrive. Holme Park Farm consists of a cluster of old buildings surrounded by fields of rough pasture. Commanding Wolf to stay at the main gate, you start up the gravel track leading from the road to the farmhouse. You spot movement. There are people here! There's a lorry parked alongside the barn, washing hanging out to dry on a line and nearby, in the field by the house, you see two women. Emotion floods your body and you feel light-headed with relief.

When they see you, the women start running back towards the farmhouse.

The decisions you make now will decide whether you live or die.

➜ If you want to run after them before they get into the house, go to 66.

➜ If you want to stop, put your hands up to show you are harmless and shout a greeting, go to 1.

➜ If you want to walk after the women, go to 19.

48.

The cash register has been emptied and hangs open. Behind the counter there are several things hanging on the shelves, but in the gloom you can't quite see them. On the end of the aisle there are some tinned products on the shelves.

➜ If you want to stop to examine the shelves behind the counter more closely, go to 11.

➜ If you'd prefer to keep moving down the aisle, go to 58.

49.

You move further behind the drums, but now you can't see where Whiley is standing. Before you have time to move back, Whiley appears with his rifle raised. The muzzle flashes and you crash back onto the icy ground.

➜ Whiley has killed you! Get back to Chapter 6 to try again.

50.

You slow down.

"Keep away. You could be infected,"

the man shouts. You can see other people behind him, peering out of the windows.

➡ If you want to continue to approach with caution, go to 34.

➡ If you'd rather stop, go to 8.

51.
You grab a branch, but it cracks and gives way. You tumble into the freezing water. Go to 65.

52.
A dog pounces and you swing your axe. There is an awful crunching noise as the metal head connects, and the dog crashes down dead. But another dog leaps, and another. Wolf savages one of them, but they just keep coming. Other dogs pull at you from behind, toppling you over, and it's not long before your screams that fill the air are abruptly silenced.

➡ You are dead — you've failed to survive. Get back to try Chapter 3 again.

53.

You open the can and throw the contents at the dog. It smells fruity, and the dog shows no interest. Go to 85.

54.

You try to explain that you're hungry and have cycled a long way, when without further warning a bullet slams into your chest. You crumple over, gasping for breath. As your vision fades, the long-haired man from the house stands over you. "I gave you a choice," he says.

➜ You have failed the challenge. Go back to Chapter 4 to try again.

55.

Wolf runs towards you. For a second, his lead pulls tight, then he pulls the gatepost free and the lorry begins to roll. Everything seems to happen in slow motion; the lorry rolls forward and the rope trailing from it starts to pull. You mustn't let Whiley realise what's about to happen. The only thing you can do is get Whiley's attention yourself.

➡ You'll have to rely on luck, go to either 30 or 70.

56.

The car is in the middle of the road, but Peter slumps across the wheel again. You feel a jolt as the car starts rolling over the grassy verge on the other side of the road.

➡ If you want to pull the handbrake, go to 71.

➡ If you want to try to press your foot on the clutch pedal to disengage the engine, go to 39.

➡ If you think pulling the steering wheel will get the car back onto the road, go to 44.

57.

There are just three dogs in front of you, and Wolf's snarling keeps them back as you walk swiftly down the street. But the three are tracking you, and just then a larger pack emerges from behind another car.

➡   To try to get into one of the cars, go to 84.

➡️ To start running forwards, go to 14.

➡️ To stand and try to fight them off with your axe, go to 52.

➡️ To head back to the electrical shop with the van sticking half-through the window, go to 45.

58.

You walk forward carefully, one step at a time. You are taken completely by surprise when a dark shape leaps out at you.

➡️ If you have a torch, go to 72.

➡️ If you don't have a torch, go to 16.

59.

You got away, but you feel emotionless and deflated. You need the company of other people, but these have made it clear that all you are to them is a source of infection. If Alex had been there things would have been different. You and Wolf head away from the farm when you hear a shout.

"Hey!"

You turn and spot a skinny woman
striding purposefully out of the farmhouse.
Her skin is white, her eyes are sunken.
She shouts, "Is that you?"

The man with the handgun grabs her
arms and pins them at her sides. Now she's
screaming.

"That's my sister's child!"

"Alex?" You turn back towards the farmhouse.

"Not one step further or I'll shoot!"

"Mum, Dad, Laura?" you plead. "Are they all right?"

Alex is struggling. She frees one of her arms.

"Laura's here!"

Alex's words are cut off by the long-haired man who followed her out. He strikes her across the back of the head, and she drops to her knees.

"Please let me see my sister!" you shout, edging closer to the house.

A shot rings out, and this time you turn and run.

CHAPTER FIVE

Your mind is racing as you retrieve your BMX and pedal furiously away. Wolf runs along beside you. You feel overjoyed at finding out that Laura survived, but this is tempered with the despair that seeing her will probably get you killed. And there's Alex. She's being held against her will in her own house. And she's ill. She could be dying.

A month passes and the weather has turned colder as winter settles in. Worst of all, you've run out of food. Faced with either dying of starvation or heading back to town and fighting the dog packs, you muster up the courage to go back to Holme Park Farm.

Back at the farm, you walk slowly through the gate. It surprises you when you find no one on guard. You hold your arms out wide, daring anyone to challenge you, but nobody does. You make it to the front door and knock, and when there's no answer you walk around the building and peer through the windows.

The house is still lived in — that much is clear — but it's messier than you had imagined it, with empty tins of food left out on tables and a sink full of washing-up. You're suddenly aware that Wolf is alert.

"Danger?" you whisper.

Wolf tilts his head.

"You smell something?"

His tail wags. Then he's barking and

spinning around as a mound of coats and woolly hats comes bounding out of the door. You stagger backwards and almost fall over. It's Laura!

"I saw you from the window. When they shot at you, I thought you'd gone and left forever."

Laura hugs you until you can hardly breathe.

"I was so ill — and when I got better I found Alex had died and everyone else had left. It was really awful."

Her words come between sobs as she starts crying. Finally, she stops, pushes herself back and sizes you up.

"You look really scrawny," she says decisively. "And that dog you've got. It's just a bag of bones. Come here, boy," she coos, stroking Wolf's head and tickling his throat in a way you would never dare to.

"Can't have you starving," she giggles, skipping inside to return moments later with a grisly mess of bones — and Wolf settles down for a feast.

Laura pulls you into the kitchen and an awkward silence descends. She's staring at you again and it's clear she's building up courage to say something that you've already guessed at before she starts.

"I buried Alex over there," she mumbles with tears in her eyes, pointing out of the window to a large mound of freshly turned earth with rocks piled on top. "I'm not sad about them leaving. Their leader, Whiley, was evil. When they first came we were so happy to find that other people had survived, but then he took over." She opens a can of corned beef she's been keeping for emergencies, and you plunge a fork into it.

"Those people they brought with them — the 'work details' he called them — were slaves. Whiley and his two henchmen pointed guns and everyone else did the work. Alex tried to argue back, but they were armed and she was ill. They've gone now, but they left some drums of fuel, so I think they'll be back. I haven't seen Mum or Dad since I left our house."

Over the next week you size up Holme Park Farm as a place to survive the winter. There's firewood for keeping the place warm, some cabbages and potatoes in the vegetable patch behind the farm, and a river nearby with a supply of fresh water and fish. There's even a jeep (which would be great for transport if you knew how to drive it) and the drums of petrol and diesel that Whiley left behind. But, there just isn't enough food. Whiley and his gang took most of Alex's stores when they moved on and the few of the farm's sheep that they didn't shoot have fled. Laura's been keeping going on mutton stew, made from one of the dead sheep. But that is almost finished now and when, one icy afternoon, just before sunset, you spot a lone roe deer rooting through the snow down by the river, your eyes light up and your mouth waters at the thought of fresh meat. You grab a rope lasso and a long knife, whistle for Wolf to come along and set off in pursuit.

Survival Challenge: Deer Hunt

A shelf of clear ice has formed over the edge of the stream and the deer has dashed onto this. For a moment it hesitates, looking back at you, undecided whether to jump across the water gap. You can see it tensing its body.

The decisions you make now will decide whether you live or die.

➜   If you want to wait with Wolf to see what the deer does, go to 23.

➜   If you want to let Wolf follow it onto the ice, go to 5.

➜   If you'd prefer to chase the deer across the ice to try to lasso or stab it with your knife, go to 12.

60.

Flames track along the spilt petrol, reaching the drums. As the nearest one explodes you are blasted sideways. Whiley steps back and bursts out laughing. Go to 20.

61.

Peter is awake enough to push your hands off the wheel, but now he's not looking where he is going. Go to 3.

62.

You set off the fire extinguisher and it sprays a jet of super-cooled carbon dioxide right into the mouth of a huge Doberman with slavering jaws. This stuns it long enough for you to reach for the door handle of the fire exit. Go to 47.

63.

Whoompf! the fuel ignites, and a ball of flame shoots upwards. Whiley turns away as he shields himself from the heat. Go to 90.

64.

The dog knocks you to the floor, and you drop your hammer. You scream as its teeth tear into you. You fight briefly, but you are too weak, and soon you are overcome by the pain. You die in the shop as the dog feasts.

➜ You have died a grisly death. Go back to Chapter 2 to try again.

65.

The current has hold of you, sweeping you, Wolf and the deer downstream.

➜ To swim for the riverbank, go to 89.

➜ To go for the deer, which is only just beyond your reach, go to 77.

63

64

65

66.

The women run into the farm's front door past a man with a scarf over his mouth. He points a handgun at you.

➡ To carry on chasing after the women, go to 34.

➡ To slow down, but keep on walking, go to 50.

➡ To run away, go to 76.

67.

The last you see of the deer is its antlers disappearing off downstream. It's a shame you lost your meal, but at least Wolf manages to get out of the water and rejoin you. Go to 78.

68.

You duck down behind the counter, but dogs are streaming into the shop through the broken window — and they are heading straight for your hiding place. Go to 24.

66

67

68

69.

The deer is trying to swim across but it is taken by the river's current. Wolf leaps in after it. Go to 9.

70.

You leap out and Whiley shoots. The bullets thud into your unprotected body. Wolf leaps up to defend you, but Whiley shoots him too. The dog yelps before collapsing in a heap, blood pouring from his wounds. You die together in the cold dirt.

➜   Whiley has killed you. Go back to Chapter 6 to try again.

71.

You pull the handbrake and the car jerks sideways. The car skids, the tyres squealing on the road. Do you want to release the handbrake?

➜   To release the handbrake, go to 81.

➜   If you'd rather keep the handbrake on, go to 40.

72.

It's a massive guard dog! You see it in the torchlight just in time to pull back. Its snarling jaws miss your face, but then it launches itself at you. You stagger back.

The dog suddenly falls to the floor with a yelp, and it's only then that you see it is restrained by a long chain. But the dog is powerful and is slowly pulling the chain. It's getting closer. The chain is slipping!

➜ To hit the dog with your hammer, go to 79.

➜ To feed it some packet meat from the fridge, go to 88.

➜ If you picked up some cans of tinned meat, go to 27.

73.

You wake up at the water's edge. Wolf is nuzzling your face and whining. He starts licking you and yelping for joy when he sees your eyes open. You are alive, but you had better get moving and warm up soon before hypothermia sets in. Go to 78.

74.

You stop and heave the heavy extinguisher over your head. You turn and throw it down right onto the head of the lead dog, a huge Doberman with a jagged bite mark across its muzzle. That one's down, but there are more dogs coming. Go to 24.

75.

You pull the steering wheel and speed past the lorry, just as a tanker comes round the corner. You steer out of the way, but you're still speeding forward. How will you stop safely?

➡ To pull the handbrake, go to 40.

➡ To press your foot on the clutch pedal to disengage the engine, go to 17.

➡ To pull the steering wheel and turn the car off the road, go to 28.

76.

As you turn and run towards the gate, you hear bullets strike the path by your feet.

➡ To stop running and put your hands up, go to 87.

➡ To keep on running, go to 59.

77.

You try to reach the deer but somehow it just manages to stay out of your reach. You're starting to feel very tired. Go to 42.

78.

You are numb with cold — and it is getting dark. You gather up your rope and, with Wolf alongside you, you start running back towards the Holme Park Farm. You hear gunshots and the sound of a lorry engine coming from the farm. Even before you arrive, you know that Whiley is back.

CHAPTER SIX

It's fully dark by the time you get back up the hill to the farm. In the moonlight you can see the blocky outline of Whiley's lorry reverse-parked on the sloping driveway

between the house and the large barn.
You know Whiley has returned for the fuel,
and you know that if he finds Laura alive
and well, he'll take her too. You have to
stop him.

There is someone in the lorry. You can see the outline of a man's head and upper body behind the steering wheel silhouetted by a light inside. Whiley? You doubt it. You would expect the boss to be in the house, not on guard. If this man is meant to be watching out for you coming back, then he has made a big mistake. Having a light on behind him has not only given his position away, it will have also dulled his night vision.

Crouching low and keeping to the shadows, you reach the double doors at the rear of the lorry without being spotted. You notice that to prevent the truck rolling forwards, someone has placed a length of gatepost under the rear wheels on the opposite side to the driver. The post is loosely held and could be pulled away quite easily. Also, now you can hear hushed voices coming from the back of the lorry. Whiley has more slaves! You realise you can free whoever is being held captive by just lifting a metal bar wedging the two doors together. Not yet though. You have to remove Whiley's henchman in the cab from the scene, and you aim to get rid of Whiley too. Both men are larger, stronger and better armed than you, but you have the element of surprise, a rope — and the truck is on a slope. A plan quickly hatches in your head.

You sneak up to the front of the house. There you knot one end of your rope into a free-running loop, which you place over the mat beneath the doorstep. You then tie the other end to the lorry's rear bumper. Your trap is set. Now, to work on a distraction. For that you will need the fuel.

You open the top of one of the drums marked "P" and lean it over slightly so that fuel sloshes onto the ground. Then you take off your coat and soak one of the sleeves.

This will be your firelighter. You leave it on top of one of the oil drums for now. As for Wolf, you order him to "stay" by the back wheel of the truck. You tie his lead to the gatepost that is stopping the wheels from rolling down the hill. Finally, you rush to the back of the lorry, lift the bar and open the doors.

"You're free," you say, barely having time to register the ten or so people huddled in the darkness inside.

"Get out now!"

You run to the passenger door. As the driver gets out to check what the noise is at the back, you climb into the cab, release the handbrake and pull the keys from the ignition. That done, you slip out, locking both doors of the cab as you leave. Now you head back to the fuel drums.

The driver is fully occupied as you had hoped he would be. By the time he reaches the back of the lorry, two girls have already got out. There is shouting and you hear a gunshot. You had hoped the man wouldn't be armed, but you go on with your plan nonetheless. You pull the lighter out of your pocket and set fire to your petrol-soaked coat.

Survival Challenge: The Fight for the Farm

If the gunshot hadn't got the attention of the people inside the farmhouse, then the sight of flames has. Whiley — the long-haired thug — appears at the door holding his automatic rifle. His eyes are flitting between you with the flaming coat and the growing mass of people at the back of the truck who are now jostling the henchman with the gun. Then Whiley fires into the air, and the noise instantly hushes the crowd.

"Unless you stop now, there will be killing," he shouts.

For your trap to work, you need him to take one step forward onto the doormat.

The decisions you make now will decide whether you live or die.

➜ If you want to set light to the drums of fuel, go to 60.

➜ If you want to tell Wolf to "Kill", go to 20.

➜ If you want to stall for time and shout at Whiley, go to 83.

79.
You swing your hammer and it catches the dog in the head. The dog goes wild, and as it thrashes around, the chain comes loose. The dog hurls itself at you. Go to 64.

80.
"Stop right there," an armed man at the door shouts.

➜ If you want to do as he says, go to 8.

➜ If you want to get closer, go to 34.

81.

Peter's foot is still jammed hard on the accelerator and you are still going too fast! Your eyes snap to the road ahead. There's an abandoned lorry blocking the lane!

You can't reach past Peter to pull out the ignition key, and you can't get out of the car at this speed.

➜ If you want to avoid the lorry by pulling the handbrake, go to 13.

➜ To press your foot on the clutch pedal to disengage the engine, go to 32.

➜ To avoid the lorry by pulling the steering wheel to move the car, go to 75.

82.

Shining the torch you see that some of the tins have fruit in, while others contain tinned meat. All the cans have ring-pulls on the top, so they can be opened easily. You take a couple of each. Go to 58.

83.

You shout, "I want my farm back. I want

my sister." Whiley slowly raises his gun and takes aim.

➜   To dive behind the fuel drums, go to 7.
➜   To set light to the fuel, go to 60.

84.

You dive into an empty car and Wolf leaps in after you. You turn and just manage to heave the door closed as a dog slams into the car. Enraged dogs leap up at the windows, so close to your face that you can see right down their throats. You and Wolf are safe where you are, but this safety is only temporary. Sooner or later, you will have to get out and face the pack.

➜   To make a run for it, go to 24.
➜   If you'd rather wait until later before leaving the car, go to 41.

85.

The dog lurches forwards, and the chain comes loose. What happens now is purely down to luck. Choose either 25 or 64.

86.

You edge forwards, but the ice gives way under your feet. Go to 65.

87.

A bullet slams into your body, your legs buckle and you crash down. You're dead before you hit the ground.

➜   You got this far, but it's all gone wrong. Go back to Chapter 4.

88.

You grab a packet of meat from the fridge — it stinks — and toss it to the dog. But the dog isn't desperate enough to eat rotting meat, not when it can smell you! Suddenly, it slips free from the chain and launches itself at your throat. You are knocked backwards as blood bubbles down your neck. You punch and struggle with the dog, but there's no way you can survive.

➜   You have been mauled to death. Go back to Chapter 2 to try again.

89.

You swim through the icy water towards the riverbank. Numbed by the cold, your limbs are starting to seize up. Luck is the only thing that can save you now. Choose either 2 or 73.

90.

The lasso pulls tight around Whiley's feet. Whiley is still squeezing the trigger, firing bullets as he is pulled to the ground. The lorry gains speed as it rolls onto the open field and heads down towards the river. The last you see of Whiley are the flashes from his gun as, still firing wildly, he is dragged down the hill.

You hear a crash and a splash, then nothing more. You untie the rope and gatepost from Wolf, and he follows you into the house. Laura is in the kitchen. She is tied to a chair and gagged, but she is safe. The back door is open, and you can just make out Whiley's other henchman running away into the darkness. You don't bother to chase him. Instead, you cut your sister's bonds and set her free.

CHAPTER SEVEN

Whiley's body was never found. The lorry
ended up in the river and, when you and
Wolf went down to check, you found the
rope snapped and no tracks to show where
he went. Perhaps he was swept away with
the current. The lorry was wrecked but you
know you can find another if you take a
trip down to town. It's a shame about the
fuel though.

There were 12 people imprisoned in
the back of the lorry. They had quickly
overpowered the lorry driver, although one
was hurt in the arm when his gun went off.
You let him go the next morning and sent
him away without his gun or his coat, even

though he pleaded to stay. You never found out what happened to the other henchman who ran away.

No one was sad to see Whiley and his gang go, and all but two of the people you set free opted to stay with you and Laura at Holme Park Farm.

There's still no sign of your mum and dad — but the hope that they might have survived helps to keep you going.

You reckon that together you can start a community and maybe find others out there who want to keep some sort of civilisation going. One thing you know for certain — you can survive.

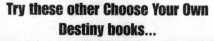